Power Maths

Year 2
Practice Book 2C

CW00540312

What have you done in maths in Year 2?

Draw or write what you enjoyed doing most.

This book belongs to _____ .

My class is _____ .

Series editor: Tony Staneff

Lead author: Josh Lury

Consultant (first edition): Professor Liu Jian and Professor Zhang Dan

Author team (first edition): Kelsey Brown, Jenny Lewis, Josh Lury, Stephen Monaghan, Beth Smith, Paul Wrangles, Liu Jian, Zhang Dan, Hou Huiying and Huang Lihua

Contents

We will practise different ways to solve problems!

It is time to continue our maths journey!

How to use this book

Do you remember how to use this Practice Book?

Use the Textbook first to learn how to solve this type of problem.

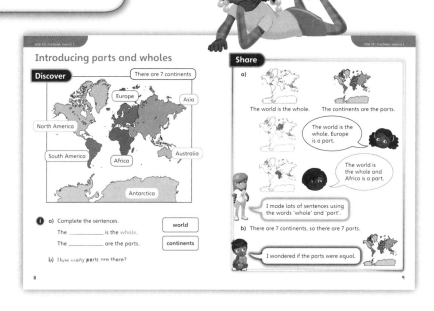

This shows you which Textbook page to use.

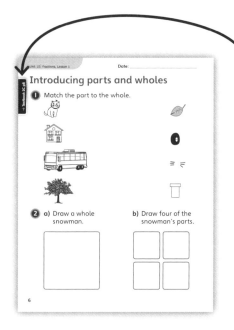

Have a go at questions by yourself using this Practice Book. Use what you have learnt.

Challenge questions make you think hard!

Questions with this light bulb make you think differently.

Reflect

Each lesson ends with a Reflect question so you can show how much you have learnt.

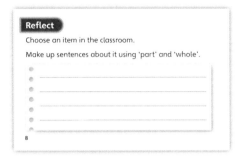

Show what you have done in My power points at the back of this book.

My journal

At the end of a unit your teacher will ask you to fill in My journal.

This will help you show how much you can do now that you have finished the unit.

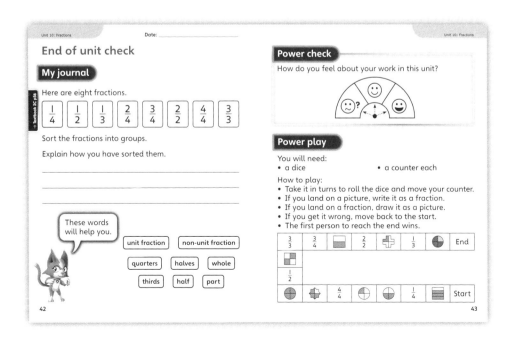

Date: _____

Introducing parts and wholes

1 Match the part to the whole.

2 **a)** Draw a whole snowman.

b) Draw four of the snowman's parts.

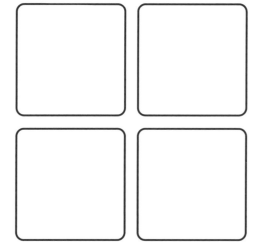

6

3 Complete the sentences about the truck.

Use some of the words in the list.

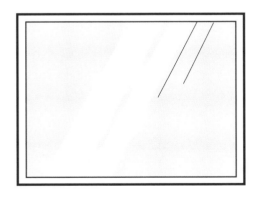

wheel	truck
light	bumper
window	

The _____ is the whole.

The _____ is a part.

The _____ is a part.

The _____ is a part.

4 A window is a part.

What could the whole be?

Can you think of three answers?

_____

_____

_____

7

5 For each image, write two sentences
about the whole and parts:

CHALLENGE

a) _____

_____

b) _____

_____

Reflect

Choose an item in the classroom.

Make up sentences about it using 'part' and 'whole'.

_____

_____

_____

_____

Equal and unequal parts

1 Complete the sentences.

a)

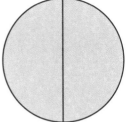

There are ☐ equal parts.

b)

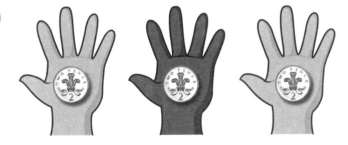

There are ☐ equal parts.

c)

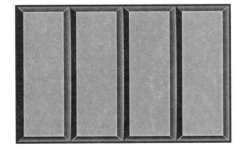

There are ☐ equal parts.

Textbook 2C p12

2 Does each picture show equal parts or unequal parts? Circle the answer.

a)

Equal parts / Unequal parts

b)

Equal parts / Unequal parts

c)

Equal parts / Unequal parts

3 Make the 4 groups equal. Draw the equal parts you find.

I can use cubes to represent the biscuits.

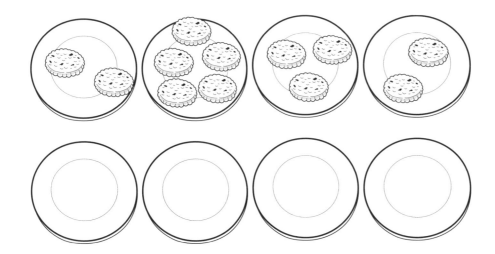

4 Draw lines to say if each shape shows equal parts or unequal parts.

CHALLENGE

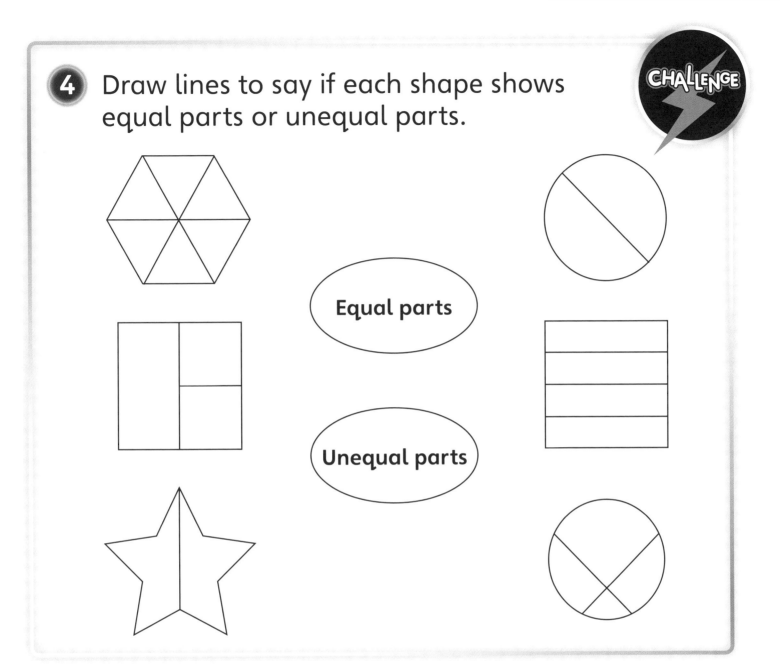

Equal parts

Unequal parts

Reflect

Get two pieces of paper.

Fold one piece into equal parts.

Fold the other piece into unequal parts.

Date: _____

Recognise a half

1 **a)** Practise writing one half.

b) Now write some more of your own.

2 Shade $\frac{1}{2}$ of each shape.

a)

c)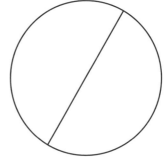

b)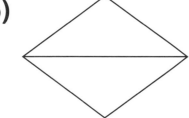

d)

3 Split each shape into halves in three different ways.

4 Tick which shapes have $\frac{1}{2}$ shaded.

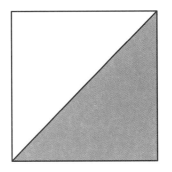 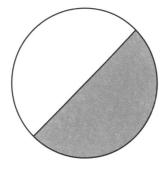 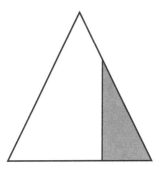

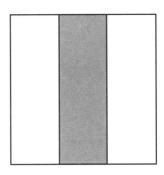 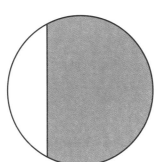 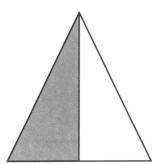

5 Circle the arrow that is pointing to $\frac{1}{2}$.

CHALLENGE

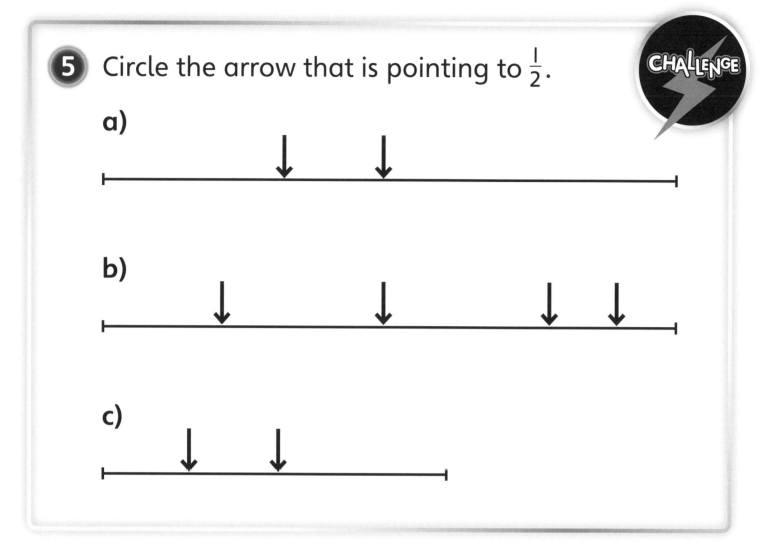

a)

b)

c)

Reflect

Fold a strip of paper in half.

Ask a partner to check that the halves are equal.

Find a half

1 Complete the number sentences.

a)

$\frac{1}{2}$ of 6 is ☐.

b)

$\frac{1}{2}$ of 8 is ☐.

c)

$\frac{1}{2}$ of 12 is ☐.

2 Complete the number sentences.

a)
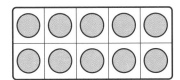
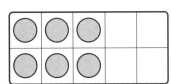

$\frac{1}{2}$ of 16 is ☐.

b)
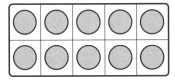
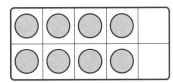

$\frac{1}{2}$ of 18 is ☐.

3 Shade $\frac{1}{2}$ of each shape.

Complete the number sentence for each one.

a)

b)

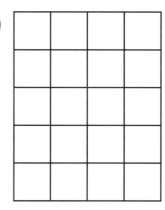

$\frac{1}{2}$ of 10 is ☐.

$\frac{1}{2}$ of 20 is ☐.

4 Circle one half of each amount.

Complete the number sentence.

a)

$\frac{☐}{☐}$ of 24 is ☐.

b)

$\frac{☐}{☐}$ of 18 is ☐.

5 Find the whole.

CHALLENGE

a) $\frac{1}{2}$ of ☐ = 3.

b) $\frac{1}{2}$ of ☐ = 11.

c) $\frac{1}{2}$ of ☐ = 7.

d) $\frac{1}{2}$ of ☐ = 13.

Reflect

Tom and Mo share these sweets.

Can they share them equally? Explain your answer.

Date: _____

Recognise a quarter

1 **a)** Practise writing one quarter.

b) Now write some more of your own.

$\frac{1}{4}$

2 Shade one quarter of each shape.

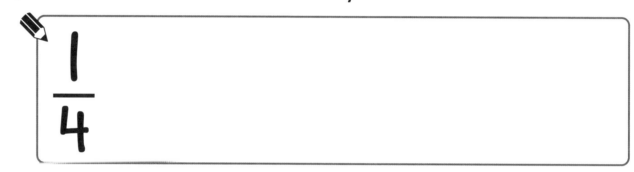

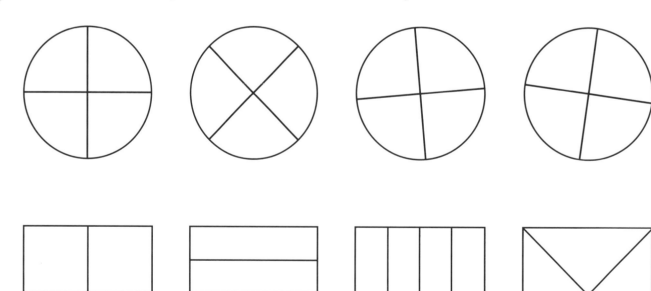

Textbook 2C p24

3 Join dots to split each shape into quarters.

a)   b)

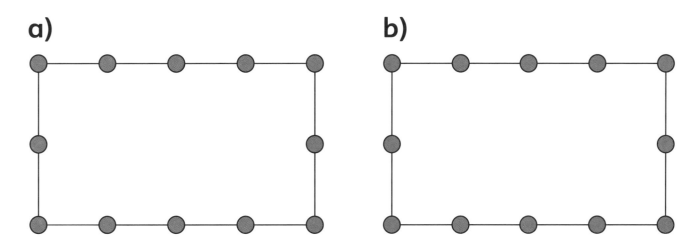

4 Circle the shapes that have $\frac{1}{4}$ shaded.

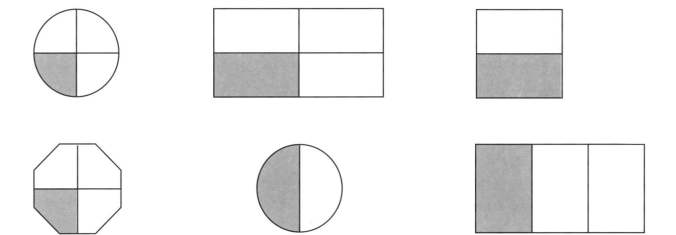

5 Split each strip into quarters.

a)

b)

6 How many different ways can you shade in $\frac{1}{4}$?

Draw more squares if you need to.

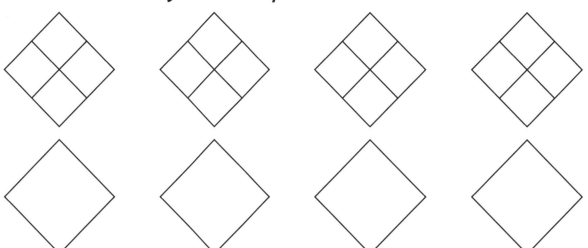

Reflect

Draw your own picture to show quarters.

Find a quarter

1 Share the counters equally into four groups.

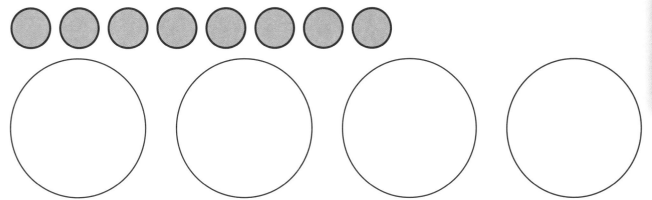

$\frac{1}{4}$ of 8 = ◻.

2 Sita has **20** flowers.

She shares them between 4 vases equally.

How many flowers are in each vase? ◻

$\frac{1}{4}$ of ◻ = ◻.

I will draw the flowers in the vases.

3 Shade $\frac{1}{4}$ of the shape.

a)
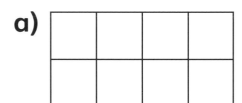

$\frac{1}{4}$ of 8 = [ ].

b)
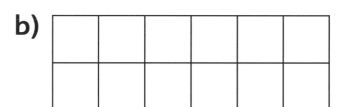

$\frac{1}{4}$ of 12 = [ ].

4 Kiki shares some sweets between 4 bags.

Complete the number sentence.

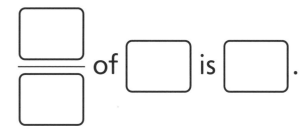 of [ ] is [ ].

5 What is $\frac{1}{4}$ of 40? [ ]

6 Draw your own picture to show $\frac{1}{4}$ of 28.

CHALLENGE

Reflect

Choose fewer than 30 counters.

Can you share your counters into 4 equal groups?

Try with different numbers of counters.

Write number sentences when you make 4 equal groups.

Date: _____

Thirds

1 **a)** Practise writing one third.

b) Now write some more of your own.

$$\frac{1}{3}$$

2 Shade one third of each shape.

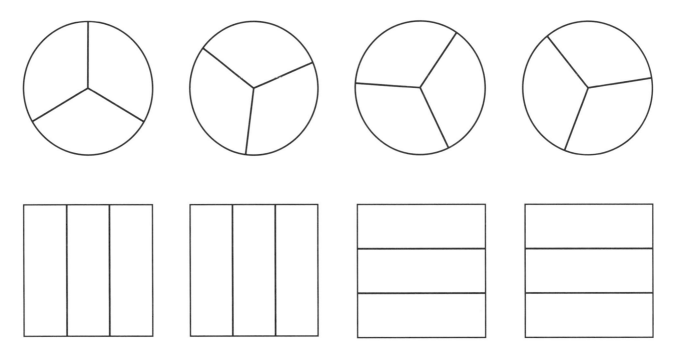

24

3 Share 18 counters into thirds.

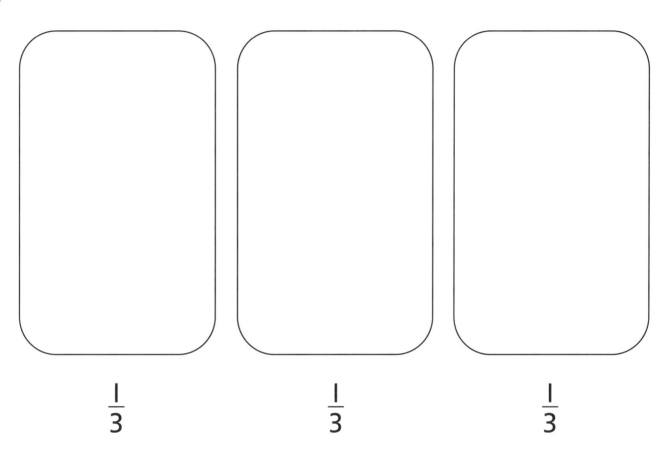

$\frac{1}{3}$　　　　　$\frac{1}{3}$　　　　　$\frac{1}{3}$

4 Split each strip into thirds.

a)

b)

c)

5 Complete the number sentences.

CHALLENGE

a)

$\frac{1}{3}$ of 9 = ☐.

b)

$\frac{1}{3}$ of 15 = ☐.

Use your answers to shade in $\frac{1}{3}$ of each shape.

Reflect

What is the same and what is different about halves, thirds and quarters? Draw a picture to show each of these fractions.

Find the whole

→ Textbook 2C p36

1 One half is 3.

What is the whole?

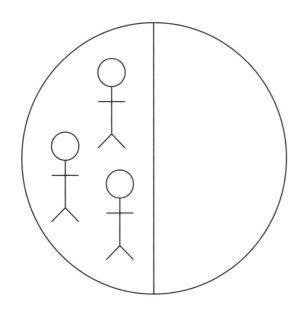

$\frac{1}{2}$ is 3.

$\frac{1}{2}$ of ⬚ = 3.

The whole is ⬚.

2 One quarter is 3.

What is the whole?

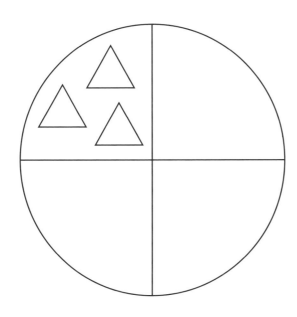

$\frac{1}{4}$ is 3.

$\frac{1}{4}$ of ⬚ = 3.

The whole is ⬚.

3 Here is one third.

What is the whole?

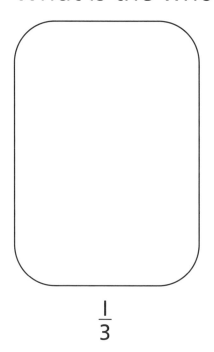  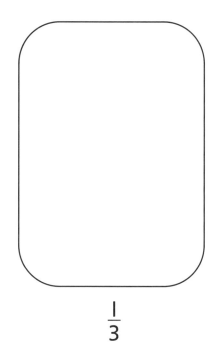

$\frac{1}{3}$ $\frac{1}{3}$ $\frac{1}{3}$

$\frac{1}{3}$ is 5.

$\frac{1}{3}$ of ☐ = 5.

The whole is ☐.

4 One quarter is 4.

What is the whole?

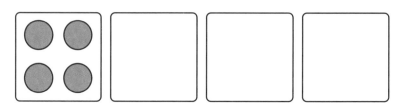

$\frac{1}{4}$ of ☐ = 4.

The whole is ☐.

5 Cassie has some marbles.

Here are half of them.

The rest are in the jar.

How many marbles does Cassie have in total?

6 a) $\frac{1}{2}$ of 10 = ☐. **b)** $\frac{1}{4}$ of 20 = ☐.

$\frac{1}{2}$ of ☐ = 10. $\frac{1}{4}$ of ☐ = 20.

CHALLENGE

Reflect

Draw a picture that shows $\frac{1}{2}$, $\frac{1}{3}$ or $\frac{1}{4}$ of an amount.

Can a partner work out the whole?

Date: _____

Unit and non-unit fractions

1 What fraction is shaded?

a)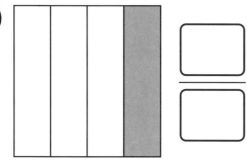

c)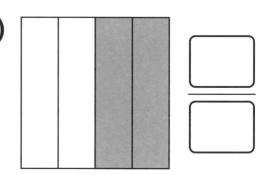

b)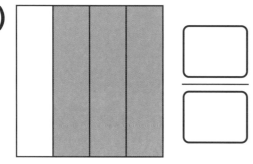

d)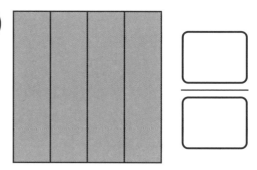

2 What fraction is shaded?

a)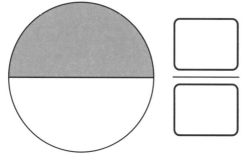

b)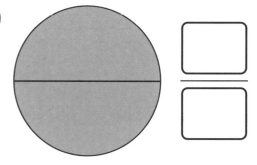

3 **a)** Shade $\frac{1}{3}$ of the shape.

b) Shade $\frac{2}{3}$ of the shape.

c) Shade $\frac{3}{3}$ of the shape.

4 **a)** Draw your own picture to show three thirds shaded.

b) Draw your own picture to show four quarters shaded.

5 Match each shaded shape to the fraction.

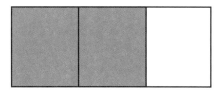

$\dfrac{2}{4}$

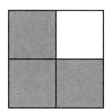

$\dfrac{2}{3}$

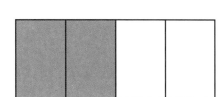

$\dfrac{3}{4}$

Reflect

Circle all the unit fractions.

$\dfrac{2}{3}$ $\dfrac{1}{4}$ $\dfrac{3}{3}$ $\dfrac{1}{2}$ $\dfrac{1}{3}$ $\dfrac{2}{4}$ $\dfrac{3}{4}$ $\dfrac{3}{3}$ $\dfrac{4}{4}$

Draw one of them.

Recognise the equivalence of a half and two quarters

1 Tick the images that have $\frac{1}{2}$ shaded.

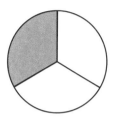 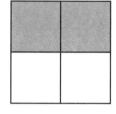 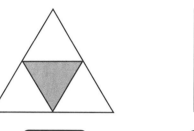 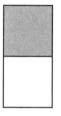

2 **a)** Shade $\frac{2}{4}$.

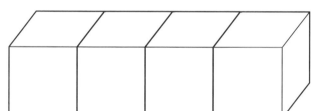

b) Shade $\frac{1}{2}$.

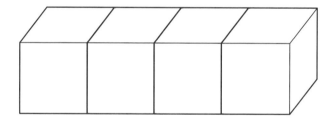

What do you notice?

_____

_____

I wonder if this is always the case.

33

3 Write the missing fractions.

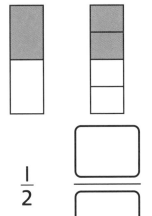 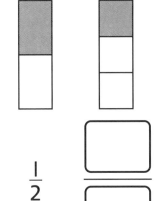 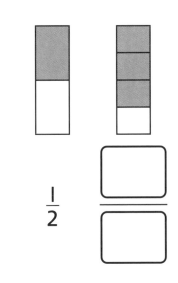

$\frac{1}{2}$

$\frac{1}{2}$

$\frac{1}{2}$

4 Shade in $\frac{2}{4}$ of each shape.

a)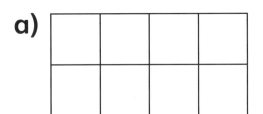

b)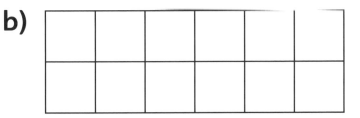

5 Harry has $\frac{2}{4}$ of the cherries.

Ali has $\frac{1}{2}$ of the cherries.

How many cherries are left?

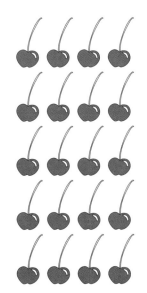

6 8 can be split into halves and quarters.

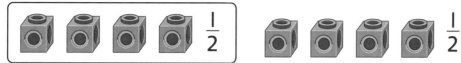 

What other amounts can be split into halves **and** quarters?

Amounts that can be split into halves and quarters	Amounts that cannot be split into halves and quarters
8	

Reflect

Use a piece of paper or cubes to show that $\frac{1}{2}$ is equal to $\frac{2}{4}$.

I used _____

I showed that $\frac{1}{2}$ is equal to $\frac{2}{4}$ by _____

_____

Date: _____

Recognise three quarters

1 Shade in $\frac{3}{4}$ of each shape.

a)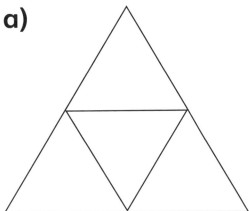

b)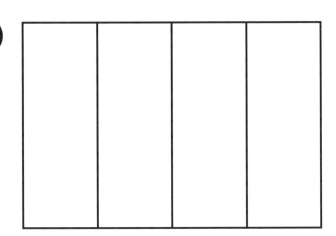

2 Shade in $\frac{3}{4}$ of each shape.

a)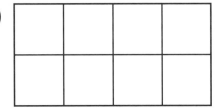

c)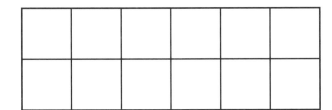

b)

d)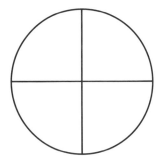

3 Tom has 12 sweets.

He shares them into four equal groups.

a) What is $\frac{1}{4}$ of Tom's sweets?

$\frac{1}{4}$ of 12 = ☐.

b) What is $\frac{3}{4}$ of Tom's sweets?

$\frac{3}{4}$ of 12 = ☐.

4 Jack has 16 brushes and 4 pots.

He puts the same number of brushes into each pot.

How many brushes are in 3 pots? ☐

5 What is $\frac{3}{4}$ of 20?

6 $\frac{3}{4}$ is 9.

a) What is $\frac{1}{4}$?

$\frac{1}{4}$ is ☐.

b) What is the whole?

The whole is ☐.

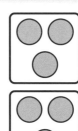

Reflect

Explain to a partner why $\frac{3}{4}$ of this shape is not shaded.

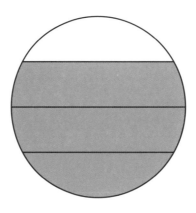

Count in fractions up to a whole

1 What fraction of each shape is shaded?

↓ Textbook 2C p52

a)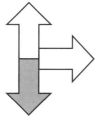

b)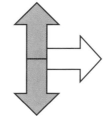

c)

2 Circle the shapes that show one whole.

3 Match the shapes to make one whole.

39

4 Circle the fractions that show a whole.

$\dfrac{1}{2}$ 　　　　 $\dfrac{2}{2}$ 　　　　　 $\dfrac{3}{4}$ 　　　　　 $\dfrac{4}{4}$

5 Complete the number sentences to describe the pictures.

a)

$\dfrac{\boxed{}}{\boxed{}} + \dfrac{\boxed{}}{\boxed{}} = \dfrac{\boxed{}}{\boxed{}} = 1$

b)

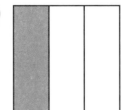

$\dfrac{\boxed{}}{\boxed{}} + \dfrac{\boxed{}}{\boxed{}} = \dfrac{\boxed{}}{\boxed{}} = 1$

6 Complete the number sentences.

a) $\dfrac{\boxed{}}{\boxed{}} + \dfrac{2}{3} = 1$

c) $\dfrac{\boxed{}}{\boxed{}} + \dfrac{2}{4} = 1$

b) $\dfrac{3}{4} + \dfrac{\boxed{}}{\boxed{}} = 1$

I wonder if I can complete this in more than one way.

7 Jemima ate 3 slices of cake.

Sam ate 2 slices of cake.

They both ate the same amount of cake.

Explain how this is possible.

Reflect

When the numerator and the denominator are the same, the fraction equals one whole.

Circle if this statement is:

always true   sometimes true   never true

Write or draw fractions to prove your answer.

Date: _____

End of unit check

My journal

→ Textbook 2C p56

Here are eight fractions.

$\frac{1}{4}$ $\frac{1}{2}$ $\frac{1}{3}$ $\frac{2}{4}$ $\frac{3}{4}$ $\frac{2}{2}$ $\frac{4}{4}$ $\frac{3}{3}$

Sort the fractions into groups.

Explain how you have sorted them.

_____

_____

_____

These words will help you.

unit fraction   non-unit fraction

quarters   halves   whole

thirds   half   part

Power check

How do you feel about your work in this unit?

Power play

You will need:
- a dice
- a counter each

How to play:
- Take it in turns to roll the dice and move your counter.
- If you land on a picture, write it as a fraction.
- If you land on a fraction, draw it as a picture.
- If you get it wrong, move back to the start.
- The first person to reach the end wins.

$\frac{3}{3}$	$\frac{3}{4}$	▬	$\frac{2}{2}$	✚	$\frac{1}{3}$	◕	End
▦							
$\frac{1}{2}$							
◉	✦	$\frac{4}{4}$	◔	◔	$\frac{1}{4}$	▤	Start

Date: _____

O'clock and half past

1 Match each clock with the correct time.

half past 2   half past 1   2 o'clock   9 o'clock

2 What time is it?

a)    It is _____ past _____.

b)    It is _____.

c)    It is _____.

3 Draw each time.

a)
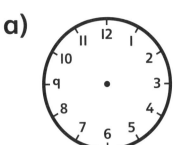
half past 11

c)
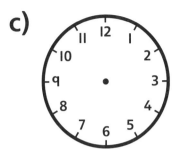
half past 6

b)
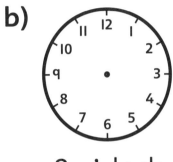
8 o'clock

d)
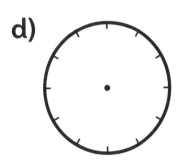
1 o'clock

4 Sam has written these answers.

half past 4

11 o'clock

half past 7

a) Tell a partner what mistakes Sam has made.

b) Draw or make the correct times on a clock.

⑤

The minute hand is pointing to the 12. The hour hand is pointing to an odd number.

CHALLENGE

What time could it be?

Try to think of as many different times as you can.

Reflect

What is always the same about these times?

○ An o'clock time always _____

○ _____ .

○ A half-past time always _____

○ _____ .

Quarter past and quarter to

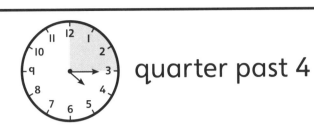 quarter past 4

 quarter to 2

Shade quarter past or quarter to on these clocks.

a) 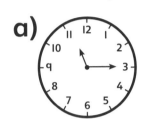 quarter past 11

b) 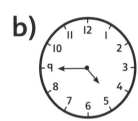 quarter to 5

2 Match each clock with the correct time.

quarter past 2

quarter to 11

quarter past 7

half past 2

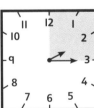

3 What time is it?

a)

_____

b)

_____

c) The minute hand is pointing to the 9. The hour hand has almost reached the 5.

_____

4 Draw the time on each clock.

a)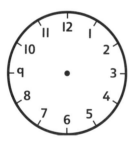

quarter past 6

c)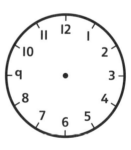

quarter to 10

b)

quarter past 8

d)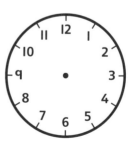

quarter to 4

48

5 Malik has tried to make quarter to 2 on this clock.

What mistake has he made?

_____

_____

6 What do the words 'past' and 'to' mean in times?

Quarter past means _____

_____.

Half past means _____

_____.

Quarter to means _____

_____.

Reflect

A 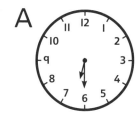 B 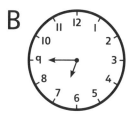 C 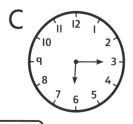 D

Which clock shows quarter to 6?

Tell a partner how you know.

Date: _____

Tell the time to 5 minutes

1 Draw the minute hand for each time.

a)

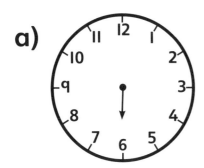

five past 6

c)

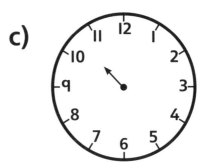

twenty-five past 10

b)

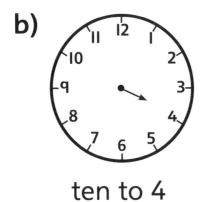

ten to 4

d)

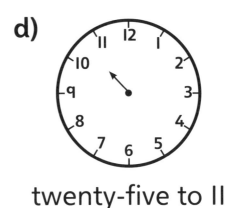

twenty-five to 11

2 Match the activities with the correct times.

ten to 7   twenty-five   twenty past 3   ten past 5
                  past 8

50

3 Tell a partner what time each bus arrives.

a)

b)

4 Draw the correct times.

a)

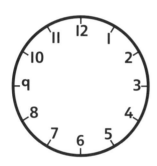

25 minutes past 2

c)

5 minutes to 10

b)

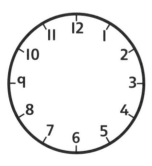

10 minutes past 7

d)

20 minutes to 3

5

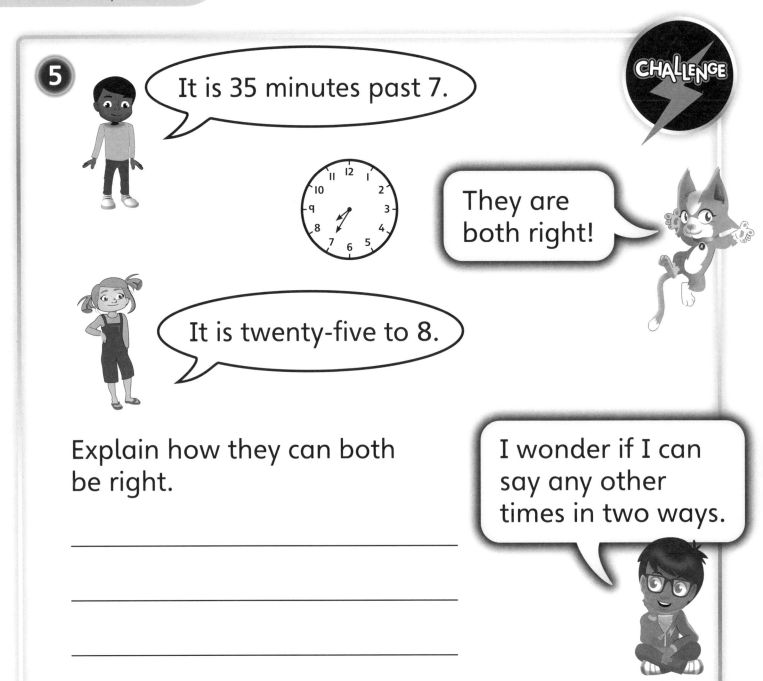

It is 35 minutes past 7.

They are both right!

It is twenty-five to 8.

CHALLENGE

Explain how they can both be right.

I wonder if I can say any other times in two ways.

_____

_____

_____

Reflect

If the time is 20 minutes past, what number will the minute hand point to? ☐

Explain to a partner how you found the answer.

Minutes in an hour

1 I hour and 5 minutes is the same as [　　] minutes.

→ Textbook 2C p72

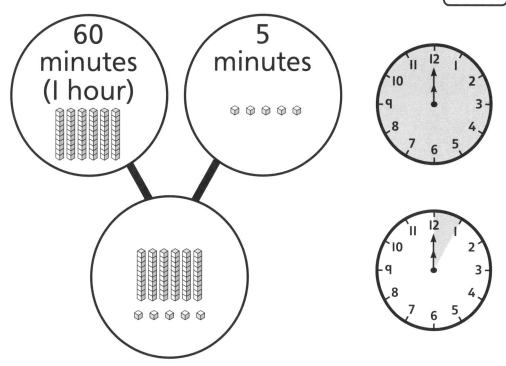

2 Show 85 minutes by shading the clocks.

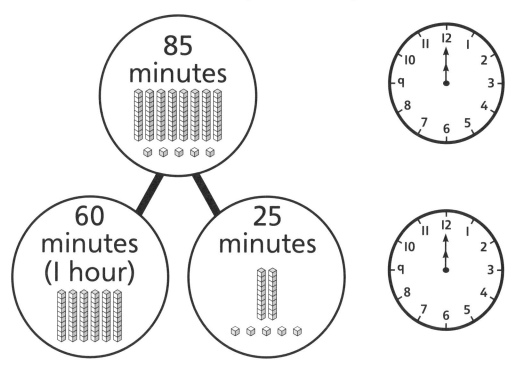

3 **a)** A film lasts for I hour and I5 minutes.

Shade in the clocks to show this.

How many minutes does the film last?

[   ] minutes

b) Another film lasts for 90 minutes.

Shade the clocks to show this.

How many hours and minutes does this film last?

[   ] hour and [   ] minutes

4 A plane flight takes more than
1 hour, but less than 77 minutes.

How many minutes could the
flight take?

CHALLENGE

Reflect

How many minutes are in 1 hour?

I think it is 12 because the numbers on a clock go up to 12!

That is not correct, but we can learn from mistakes!

How do you know the answer?

Date: _____

Hours in a day

1 Match each time with the time 24 hours later.

Wednesday

Wednesday

Tuesday

Thursday

Wednesday

Wednesday

Tuesday

Thursday

2 When is the next flight?

The next aeroplane will

leave on _____

at _____ .

Next flight in 24 hours' time

Friday

3

A bench was painted at this time on Thursday.

The paint takes 24 hours to dry.

When can you sit on the bench?

_____

_____

4 Ella has been to the dentist.
She is not allowed biscuits for the next 24 hours.

Monday morning

It is quarter to 10 on Tuesday morning.

Can Ella eat a biscuit yet? _____ .

Explain your answer to a partner.

5 The time is 11 o'clock.

CHALLENGE

During the next 24 hours, there will be more than seven different o'clock times that have a 1 in them.

Write down as many times with a 1 in as you can.

Is Ben right?

_____

Reflect

One day is when the hour hand goes once around the clock. For example, from 12 o'clock to 12 o'clock.

What is Maya's mistake?

Date: _____

End of unit check

My journal

These times have been given for you.

Explain how you know they are correct.

25 minutes
past 6

I know the time is 25 minutes past
6 because _____

_____

_____.

20 minutes to 3

I know the time is 20 minutes to 3
because _____

_____

_____.

These words
might help you.

hour hand

minute hand

Power check

How do you feel about your work in this unit?

Power puzzle

Find your way from the START to the FINISH by moving up, down, left or right.

You must only move to a time that is 20 minutes later than the one you are on!

START 4 o'clock	twenty-five past 4	ten past 5	twenty past 7
twenty past 4	twenty to 5	five past 5	twenty-five to 8
ten past 4	5 o'clock	twenty past 5	quarter to 7
half past 4	ten to 5	40 minutes past 5	half past 6
quarter to 5	quarter past 5	6 o'clock	20 minutes past 6
five to 5	twenty-five past 6	FINISH 7 o'clock	20 minutes to 7

My way, your way!

1 There are 55 children on a school trip.

There are 27 boys. How many children are girls?

There are ☐ girls.

2 A shopkeeper sells 19 apples on Saturday.
He sells 49 apples on Sunday.

How many apples does he sell in total?

The shopkeeper sells ☐ apples in total.

3 Stacey is 37. Her mum is 78.

How many years older is Stacey's mum than Stacey?

Stacey's mum is ☐ years older than Stacey.

4 Mo is watching cartoons.

'Dreams' cartoon is 32 minutes long.

'Starry Night' cartoon is 12 minutes shorter.

How many minutes long is 'Starry Night'?

'Starry Night' is ☐ minutes long.

5

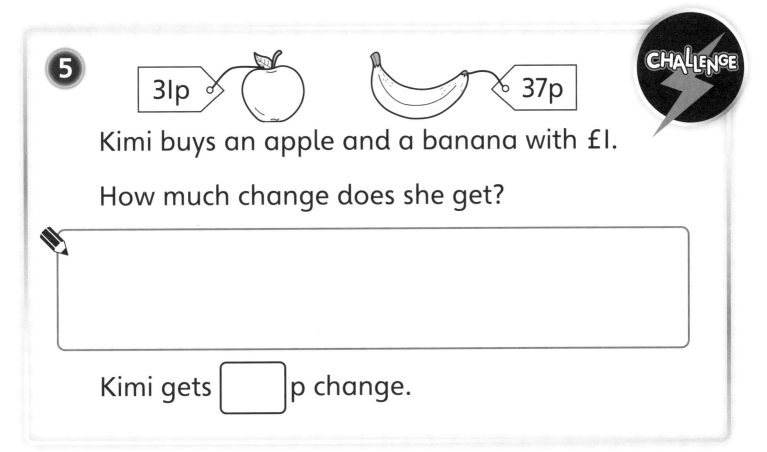

Kimi buys an apple and a banana with £1.

How much change does she get?

Kimi gets ⬚ p change.

Reflect

Oskar has £40. He is given another £35.

How much does he have in total?

I wonder what method I should use.

Oskar has £ ⬚ in total.

Date: _____

Use number facts

 a) 37 + 6 = 43

Use this calculation to help you complete these questions.

47 + 6 = ☐   57 + 6 = ☐

6 + 67 = ☐   ☐ + 6 = 33

b) 63 + 8 = 71

Use this calculation to help you complete these questions.

83 + 8 = ☐   8 + 33 = ☐

28 + 43 = ☐   ☐ + 58 = 71

2 Match the calculations that have the same answer.

30 + 5   30 + 25

50 + 5   20 + 15

60 + 5   50 + 15

Draw an arrow to show the total mass on scale B.

35 g + 45 g   15 g + 35 g

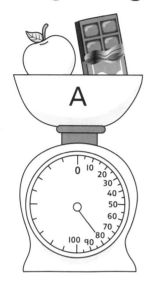   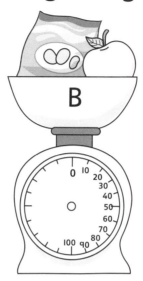

 We know that 75 + 8 = 83.

Now solve each calculation and match it to the words that describe the answer.

75 + 7   one more

65 + 8   one less

75 + 18   10 more

65 + 19   equal to

45 + 38   10 less

5 Casey has two boxes of cakes.

 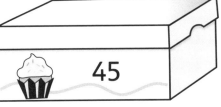 = 70

Nadia has two boxes of cakes.

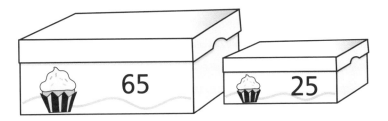

How many more cakes does Nadia have than Casey?

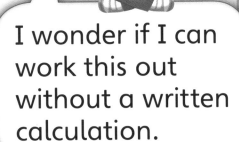

I wonder if I can work this out without a written calculation.

Nadia has ☐ more cakes than Casey.

Reflect

What is the difference between the missing numbers? Explain how you know.

$45 + \boxed{} = 60$ $45 + \boxed{} = 80$

Use a 100 square

→ Textbook 2C p92

1

1	2	3	4	5	6	7	8	9	10
11	12	13	14	15	16	17	18	19	20
21	22	23	24	25	26	27	28	29	30
31	32	33	34	35	36	37	38	39	40
41	42	43	44	45	46	47	48	49	50
51	52	53	54	55	56	57	58	59	60
61	62	63	64	65	66	67	68	69	70
71	72	73	74	75	76	77	78	79	80
81	82	83	84	85	86	87	88	89	90
91	92	93	94	95	96	97	98	99	100

Use the 100 square to complete these calculations.

a) $54 + 5 =$ ☐

b) $44 - 8 =$ ☐

c) $73 + 9 =$ ☐

d) $34 - 20 =$ ☐

2 Use the 100 square to complete these calculations.

a) $33 + 16 =$ ☐

b) $26 + 38 =$ ☐

c) $87 - 67 =$ ☐

d) $88 - 78 =$ ☐

3 Use the 100 square to complete these calculations.

a) $36 +$ ☐ $= 79$

b) $52 -$ ☐ $= 23$

c) $97 - 17 =$ ☐

d) ☐ $= 38 + 19$

67

4 Frank works out 27 + 38 on a 100 square.

1	2	3	4	5	6	7	8	9	10
11	12	13	14	15	16	17	18	19	20
21	22	23	24	25	26	27	28	29	30
31	32	33	34	35	36	37	38	39	40
41	42	43	44	45	46	47	48	49	50
51	52	53	54	55	56	57	58	59	60
61	62	63	64	65	66	67	68	69	70
71	72	73	74	75	76	77	78	79	80
81	82	83	84	85	86	87	88	89	90
91	92	93	94	95	96	97	98	99	100

> I counted on in 10s, then I counted on in 1s.

a) Show this on a number line.

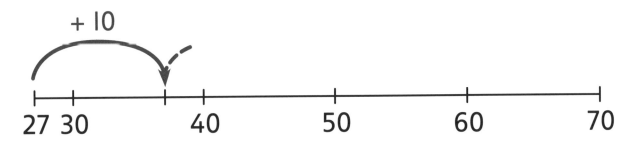

+ 10

27 30   40   50   60   70

b) Show 52 – 14 on a 100 square and a number line.

1	2	3	4	5	6	7	8	9	10
11	12	13	14	15	16	17	18	19	20
21	22	23	24	25	26	27	28	29	30
31	32	33	34	35	36	37	38	39	40
41	42	43	44	45	46	47	48	49	50
51	52	53	54	55	56	57	58	59	60
61	62	63	64	65	66	67	68	69	70
71	72	73	74	75	76	77	78	79	80
81	82	83	84	85	86	87	88	89	90
91	92	93	94	95	96	97	98	99	100

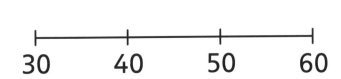

30   40   50   60

5 Some numbers have been shaded on the 100 square.

CHALLENGE

1	2	3	4	5	6	7	8	9	10
11	12	13	14	15	16	17	18	19	20
21	22	23	24	25	26	27	28	29	30
31	32	33	34	35	36	37	38	39	40
41	42	43	44	45	46	47	48	49	50
51	52	53	54	55	56	57	58	59	60
61	62	63	64	65	66	67	68	69	70
71	72	73	74	75	76	77	78	79	80
81	82	83	84	85	86	87	88	89	90
91	92	93	94	95	96	97	98	99	100

What do you notice about the 1s and the 10s?

_____

_____

Reflect

$12 + 43 = \boxed{}$

Use the 100 square to work this out, starting at 12.

Then swap the numbers and work it out again, this time starting at 43.

1	2	3	4	5	6	7	8	9	10
11	12	13	14	15	16	17	18	19	20
21	22	23	24	25	26	27	28	29	30
31	32	33	34	35	36	37	38	39	40
41	42	43	44	45	46	47	48	49	50
51	52	53	54	55	56	57	58	59	60
61	62	63	64	65	66	67	68	69	70
71	72	73	74	75	76	77	78	79	80
81	82	83	84	85	86	87	88	89	90
91	92	93	94	95	96	97	98	99	100

Discuss with a partner what you noticed about the answers.

Date: _____

Getting started

1 Use the number cards to complete the number sentences.

☐ + ☐ = 11

☐ − ☐ = 1

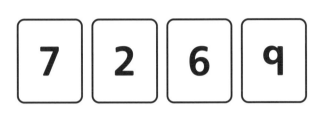

2 Find numbers to complete the number sentences.

☐ + ☐ = 16

☐ + ☐ + ☐ = 16

3

a) What is the smallest 2-digit number you can make using two of these cards? ☐

b) What is the greatest 2-digit number you can make using two of these cards? ☐

70

4 The prices of sweets are:

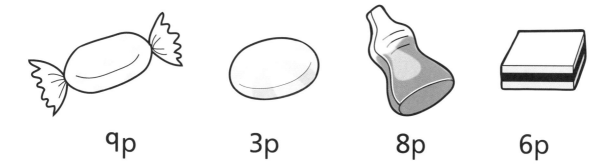

9p   3p   8p   6p

a) How much does this bag of sweets cost?

☐ + ☐ + ☐ = ☐

The bag of sweets costs ☐ p.

b) Can you make a bag of three sweets that costs 23p?

☐ + ☐ + ☐ = 23p

c) Can you make a bag of four sweets that costs 23p? (You can use each sweet more than once.)

☐ + ☐ + ☐ + ☐ = 23p

71

5 Complete these calculations.

I think there might be more than one way to do this.

a) 4☐ + ☐ = 56

b) 65 = ☐8 + ☐

Reflect

What numbers could go in the boxes?

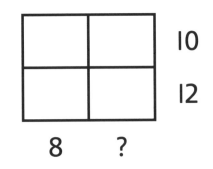

3	5	8
2	4	6

5 9

		10
		12

8 ?

Share your answers with a partner and discuss what you each did.

Missing numbers

 a) Complete the fact family shown in the part-whole model.

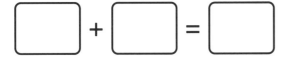

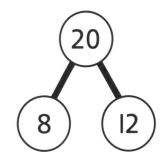

20

8   12

b) Use the number cards to create a fact family.

51 35 16

2 Write a calculation to find the missing part.

a)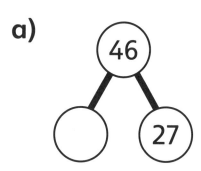

b)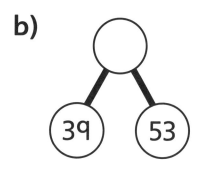

3 Work out the missing numbers.

a) ▢ + 14 = 35

c) 58 − ▢ = 24

b) 30 + ▢ = 55

d) ▢ − 42 = 26

4 Find three different ways to complete this missing number problem.

[ ] + 23 = [ ]4

Reflect

Choose a calculation to work out.

[ ] + 18 = 50

[ ] − 62 = 37

24 + [ ] = 74

81 − [ ] = 46

Explain to a partner how you solved it.

Date: _____

Mental addition and subtraction

1 Work these calculations out mentally.

a) $2 + 5 = \boxed{}$

$12 + 5 = \boxed{}$

$22 + 5 = \boxed{}$

$32 + 5 = \boxed{}$

$52 + 5 = \boxed{}$

b) $17 - 4 = 13$

$27 - 4 = \boxed{}$

$37 - 4 = \boxed{}$

$57 - \boxed{} = 53$

$\boxed{} - 4 = 83$

2 Put a cross by the calculations that must be wrong.

$45 + 3 = 47$

2 + 4 = 38

$26 + 2 = 29$

$64 - 3 = 62$

8 − 5 = 93

3 Complete these calculations.

a) 24 + 10 = ☐

24 + 30 = ☐

☐ + 50 = 94

24 + 20 = ☐

50 + 24 = ☐

b) 72 − 10 = ☐

73 − 30 = ☐

23 = 73 − ☐

72 − 20 = ☐

☐ = 73 − 50

4 Use this mental method to solve these calculations.

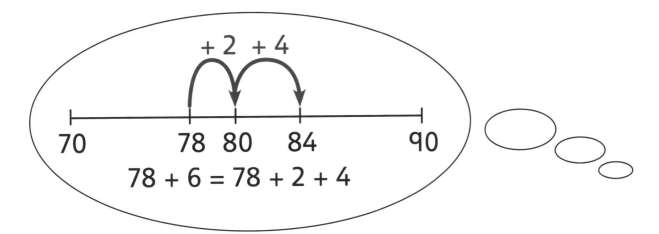

+ 2 + 4

70   78 80   84   90

78 + 6 = 78 + 2 + 4

a) 78 + 6 = ☐

b) 7 + 46 = ☐

c) 53 + 8 = ☐

d) 28 + 5 = ☐

5

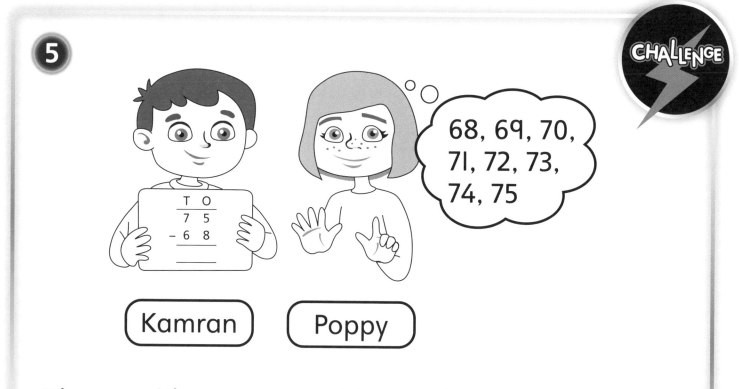

Kamran   Poppy

Discuss with a partner which method you would you use to solve 75 – 68. Explain why.

Reflect

Work out one calculation and explain to a partner how you did it.

| 34 + 4 | 34 + 20 | 79 – 5 | 79 – 55 |

Mental addition and subtraction ❷

↓ Textbook 2C p108

1 Complete these calculations.

26 + 9 = ☐   34 – 9 = ☐

43 + 8 = ☐   26 – 8 = ☐

27 + 29 = ☐   45 – 28 = ☐

> Remember to do these in your head.

68 + 28 = ☐   32 – 19 = ☐

2 Complete these calculations.

a) 78 + 18

To work this out, I can add ☐ and then

subtract ☐.

78 + 20 – ☐ = ☐

b) 26 + 59

To work this out, I can add ☐ and then

subtract ☐.

26 + 60 – ☐ = ☐

3 Samira draws this to help her answer 80 − 45.

80 − 45

$\ominus$ $\ominus$

79 − 44 = 35

Use this method to help you work out these calculations.

a) 70 − 38 = ☐

c) 90 − 49 = ☐

b) 30 − 17 = ☐

d) 100 − 26 = ☐

Explain to a partner how you got your answers.

4 Draw lines to match the calculations that give the same answers.

35 + 19	39 − 26
90 − 55	45 + 20
40 − 27	34 + 20
47 + 18	89 − 54

5 □ − □ = 26

CHALLENGE

To work out this calculation, Dylan subtracted 40 and then added 1. The answer was 26.

What calculation did he do?

Reflect

Write a top tip for adding 18.

Write a top tip for subtracting 19.

Date: _____

Efficient subtraction

1 Complete the calculations.

a) $83 - 5 = \boxed{}$

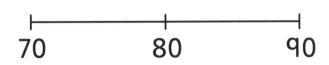

70   80   90

b) $21 - 4 = \boxed{}$

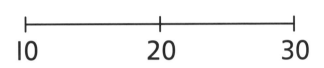

10   20   30

c) $61 - 58 = \boxed{}$

2 Work out these calculations.

a) $57 - 16 = \boxed{}$

c) $67 - 55 = \boxed{}$

b) $98 - 34 = \boxed{}$

d) $74 - 74 = \boxed{}$

3 **a)** Carlos has 92 stamps. Tilly has 80 fewer stamps.

How many stamps does Tilly have?

Tilly has ☐ stamps.

b) Barney and Marek play a game.

Their total score is 71.

Barney's score is 44. What is Marek's score?

Marek's score is ☐ points.

4 Complete these calculations.

76 – 38 = ☐   76 – 36 = ☐

76 – 37 = ☐   76 – 35 = ☐

5 Maryam works out 76 – 68.

CHALLENGE

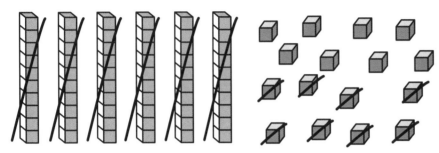

Is this the most efficient way of doing this?

Discuss with a partner a different way to work out 76 – 68.

Reflect

Discuss with a partner the best subtraction method for each of these calculations.

82 – 4 = ☐   82 – 75 = ☐   82 – 29 = ☐

Solve problems – addition and subtraction

1 Jerry buys two oranges and one banana.

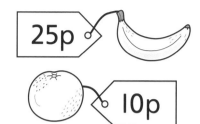

25p

10p

a) What is the total cost?

The total cost is ⬚ p.

b) How much change will Jerry get from £1?

He will get ⬚ p change.

2 Chen has **23** sweets. Annie has **4** more sweets than Chen.

How many sweets does Annie have?

Annie has ⬚ sweets.

3 Some children chose their favourite sport.

Sport	Number of children
football	16
rugby	27
tennis	11

How many more children chose rugby than chose tennis?

[ ] more children chose rugby than chose tennis.

4

12p

35p

SMILE

20p

I wonder if I can work this out without adding.

Lucy buys a balloon and a party blower.

Cooper buys a balloon and a badge.

Who spends more?

_____ spends more because _____.

5

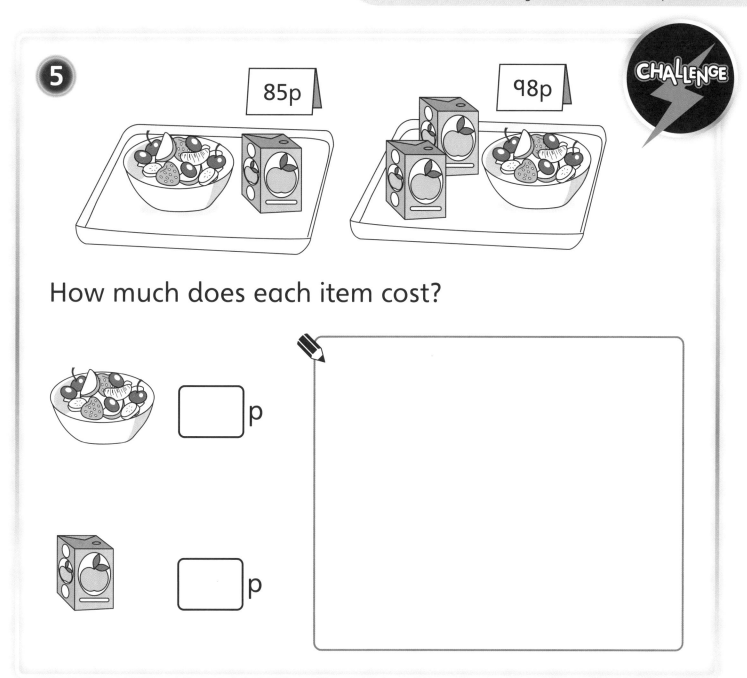

How much does each item cost?

CHALLENGE

Reflect

Make up a story for one of these calculations.

| 28 + 6 | 28 – 6 |

Tell a partner the story.

Date: _____

Solve problems – multiplication and division

1 There are six snails under each stone.

How many snails are there altogether?

There are ☐ snails altogether.

2 Mr Baker puts out eight rows of chairs.

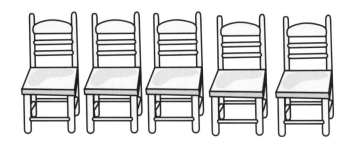

There are five chairs in each row.

How many chairs are there in total?

There are ☐ chairs in total.

88

3 Freddie needs 60 carrots for his horses.

Carrots come in bags of 10.

How many bags does Freddie need?

Freddie needs ☐ bags.

4 Max and Padma share these balloons equally between them.

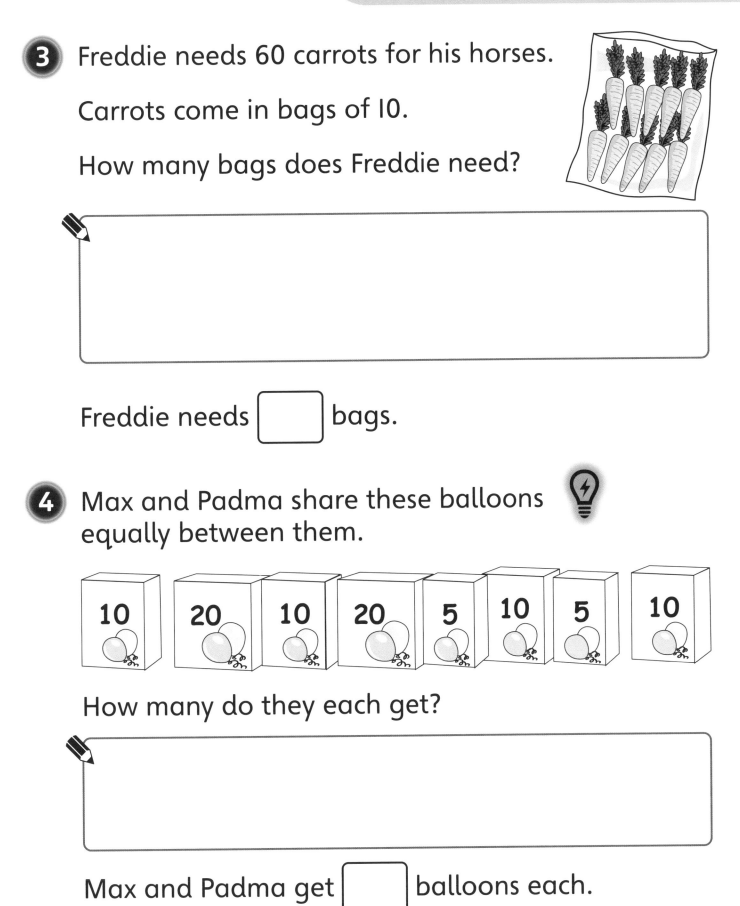

How many do they each get?

Max and Padma get ☐ balloons each.

5 Kofi has 6 toy cars.

Abby has 4 times as many cars as Kofi.

How many cars do they have altogether?

Kofi and Abby have ☐ cars altogether.

Reflect

Make a word problem for one of these calculations.

| 4 × 10 | 40 ÷ 10 |

Solve problems – using the four operations

1 Put a different number in each box to make the calculations correct.

$$\boxed{} + \boxed{} = 20$$

$$\boxed{} - \boxed{} = 10$$

$$\boxed{} \times \boxed{} = 20$$

$$\boxed{} \div \boxed{} = 10$$

2 Zac has seven . He spends .

How much does he have left?

Zac has $\boxed{}$ p left.

3 There are 40 sweets altogether.

3 children each take 5 sweets.

How many sweets are left?

[ ] sweets are left.

4 Tia wants to swim 100 m.

| 1 length = 10 metres |

She swims 6 lengths.

How many metres does she have left to swim?

Tia has [ ] m left to swim.

92

CHALLENGE

5 Calvin has 30p in altogether.

He has 12 in one hand.

How many are in his other hand?

There are ☐ in his other hand.

Reflect

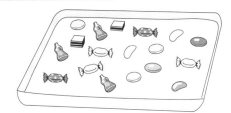

Step 1: $18 \div 2 = 9$

Step 2: $9 - 5 = 4$

Can a partner solve your story?

Write a story problem that needs both steps.

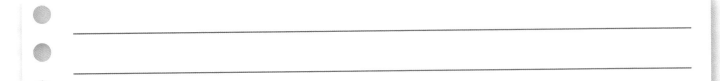

Date: _____

End of unit check

My journal

Explain the steps you need to solve this question.

Oranges are packed into boxes of 4.

I have 10 boxes of oranges.

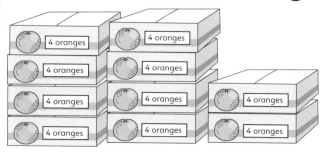

The oranges are then put into bags of 5.

How many bags of 5 oranges will I have?

First I _____

_____ .

Then I _____

_____ .

I got the answer _____ .

Power check

How do you feel about your work in this unit?

Power play

Hansel and Gretel go into the woods.

Hansel has 26 pieces of bread. Gretel has 24 pieces of bread.

How many pieces of bread do they have in total?

Hansel drops 13 pieces on the floor and Gretel drops 7 pieces.

How many pieces of bread are left in total now?

They meet 5 birds and share the rest of the bread out equally. How many pieces of bread do 3 of the birds get altogether?

95

Date: _____

Language of position

1 Here are some pictures.

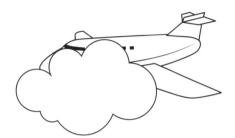

Complete sentences about the pictures.

_____ is above _____.

_____ is below _____.

_____ is next to _____.

_____ is behind _____.

2 Write sentences to describe the positions.

Use words from the word list.

top

middle

bottom

between

beside

left

right

_____

_____

_____

_____

_____

_____

3 Describe the position of an object in your classroom.

CHALLENGE

_____

_____

_____

_____

_____

Can your classmates guess what it is?

Reflect

Write some position words.

Draw pictures to show what they mean.

Describe movement

↓ Textbook 2C p136

1

a) Which person is standing to the left of ?

☐

b) Which person is standing between 🎽1 and 🎽3 ?

☐

2 **a)** Complete the sentence.

The _____ is above the cup.

b) Kim puts a flower below the picture frame.

Draw the flower on the shelf.

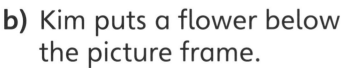

c) Explain the position of the flower to a partner in a different way.

3 Complete the sentences.

a) The cube is between the

_____ and _____ .

b) The cylinder is on top of the

_____ and the _____ .

4 Start at the shaded square.

Follow the instructions in each square you land on.

Number the squares in the correct order.

2 right, I down	I right, 2 down	2 left, I down
I right, I up	I right, I up	2 left, I down
I right, I up	I left, 2 up	I left

5 Follow the instructions and draw shapes to complete the grid.

The circle is above the square.

The square is to the right of the triangle.

The rectangle is to the left of the circle.

Reflect

Here is a grid.

Describe the position of the star to a partner.

Is there another way to describe the position of the star?

○ I could say _____

○ _____

○ _____ .

○

Date: _____

Describe turns

1 Circle the correct word in each sentence.

a)

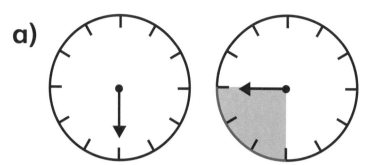

The arrow moved a quarter turn
clockwise / anticlockwise.

b)

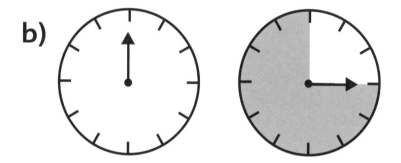

The arrow moved a three-quarter turn
clockwise / anticlockwise.

c)

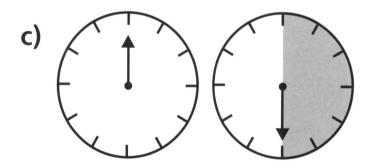

The arrow moved a half turn
clockwise / anticlockwise.

↑ Textbook 2C p140

2 Complete the sentences to describe the turns.

a)

The ladybird moved a _____
turn clockwise.

b)

The ladybird moved a _____
turn anticlockwise.

c)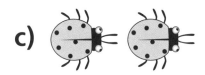

The ladybird moved a _____
turn clockwise.

3 Match each image to the correct description.

Quarter turn clockwise

Whole turn anticlockwise

Half turn clockwise

4 Here is a fly. It has turned clockwise.

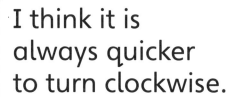

I think it is always quicker to turn clockwise.

Do you agree with Ash?

Circle your answer and explain.   Yes / No

_____

_____

Reflect

Here is a house.

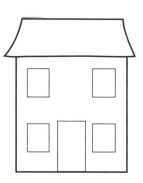

Draw the turns in the boxes below.

Half turn clockwise	Three-quarter turn anticlockwise	Quarter turn clockwise

Describe movement and turns

1 The pirate moves to the treasure.

Put an X where the treasure is.

Instructions to find the treasure:

Forwards 2
Quarter turn clockwise
Forwards 1

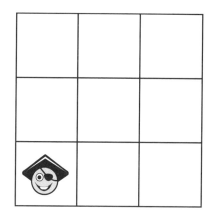

2 Complete the sentences to get the bee to the nest.

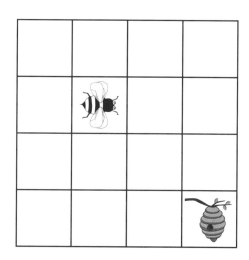

clockwise
anticlockwise
forwards
backwards
quarter

Go ☐ spaces _____ .

Make a _____ turn

_____ .

Go ☐ spaces _____ .

3 Match each image to the correct instructions to get from Start to the tortoise.

a)

Forwards 2, quarter turn anticlockwise, forwards 1

Forwards 2, quarter turn clockwise, forwards 2

Forwards 1, quarter turn clockwise, forwards 1

b) Create your own instructions for the grid below.

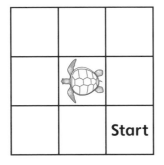

You could start with a turn or you could start by moving forwards.

_____

_____

4 Is Rico correct? How do you know?

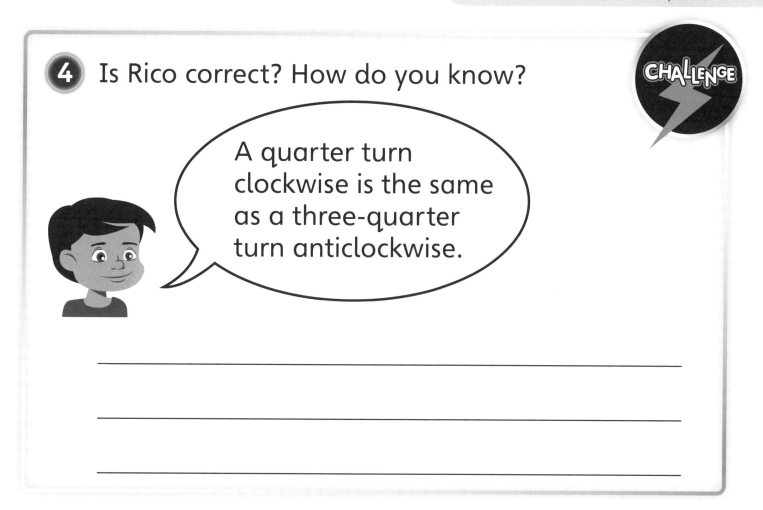

CHALLENGE

_____

_____

_____

Reflect

Draw the arrow in a different position.

Can a partner describe
how you have turned it?

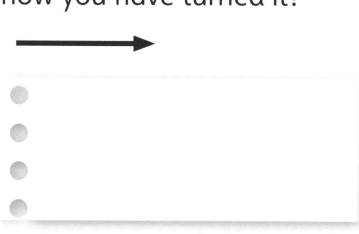

I will try to describe
my partner's arrow
in two ways.

107

Date: _____

Make patterns by turning shapes

1 Circle the shape that goes in the space.

a)

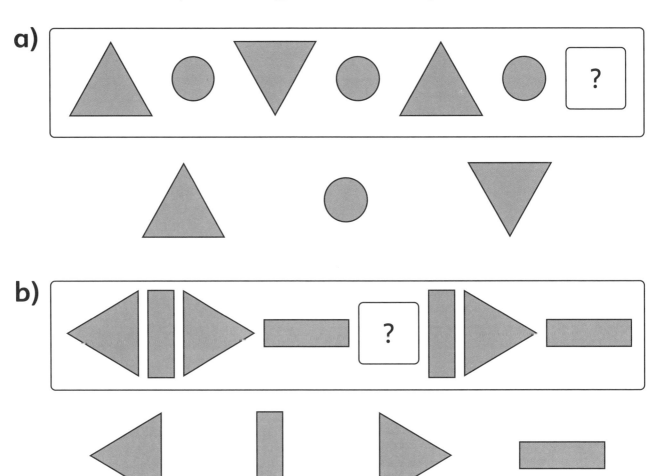

b)

2 Draw the missing shape in each pattern.

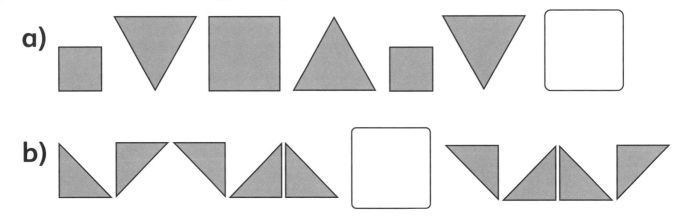

a)

b)

3 Draw the next two shapes in each pattern.

a)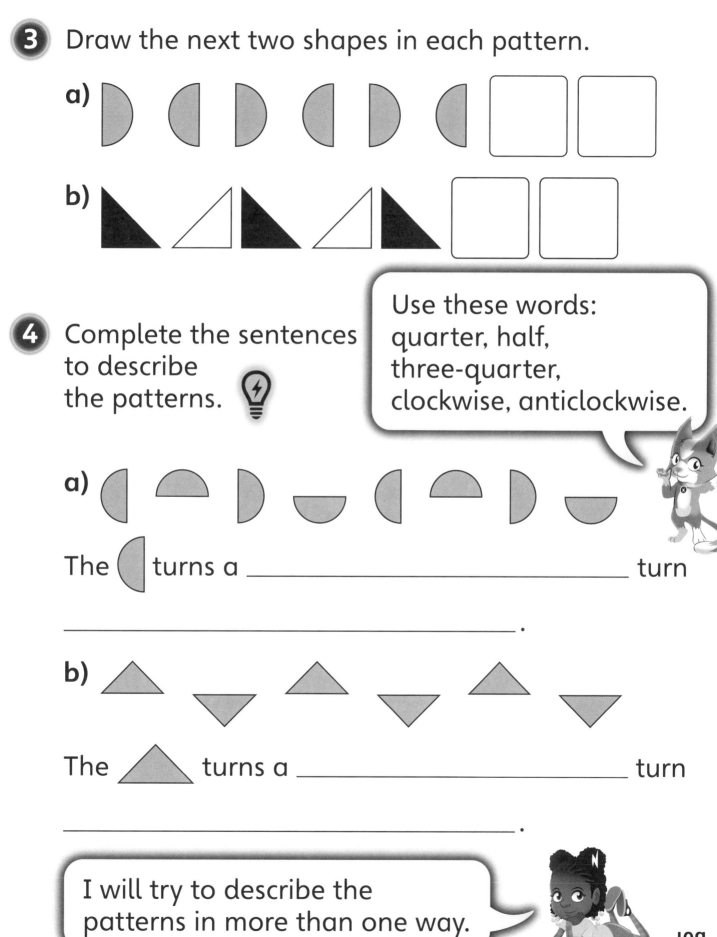

b)

4 Complete the sentences to describe the patterns.

Use these words: quarter, half, three-quarter, clockwise, anticlockwise.

a)

The ◖ turns a _____ turn

_____.

b)

The ▲ turns a _____ turn

_____.

I will try to describe the patterns in more than one way.

CHALLENGE

5 Circle the odd one out.

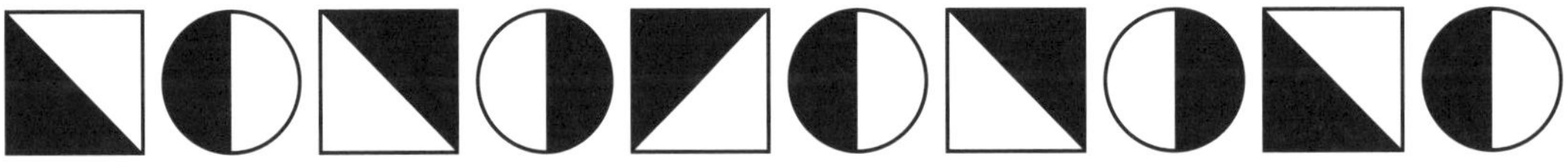

Explain how you know this is the odd one out.

____

____

Reflect

Trace around two different shapes.

Make a repeating pattern for a partner to describe.

End of unit check

My journal

Ask a partner to choose an item.

Write some questions you could ask to work out which item they have chosen.

For example: Is it on the top row?

_____

_____

_____

_____

_____

These words will help you.

left	right
above	below
top	bottom

Power check

How do you feel about your work in this unit?

Power play

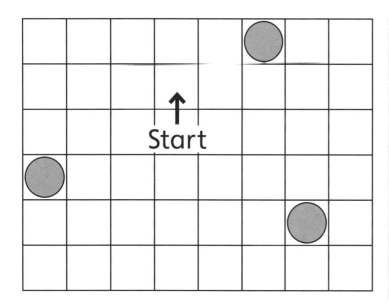

= move forwards 1
= move forwards 2
= move backwards 1
= move backwards 2
= quarter turn clockwise
= quarter turn anticlockwise

- Begin at the Start square and roll a dice to find out how to move.

- Take it in turns to roll the dice.

- The first person to land on a grey circle wins.

- If you cannot finish a move, you miss a turn.

Make tally charts

1 A group of children were asked to pick their favourite pet animal.

a) Complete the tally chart.

Animal	Tally	Number
cat	|||| |||| |||| ||||	
dog	|||| |||| |||| ||	
hamster	|||| |||| |||	
fish	|||| ||||		

b) Which animal was the most popular?

_____

c) Which animal was the least popular?

_____

d) How many more people chose dog than chose hamster?

2 20 children used a ball to show which was their favourite sport.

a) Complete the tally chart to show the results.

Sport	Tally	Number
football		
rugby		
tennis		
cricket		

b) Which sport was the least favourite?

_____

c) How many children chose cricket?

d) How many children in total chose football or rugby?

3 Complete the tally chart. Then write three statements about it.

CHALLENGE

Preferred pizza toppings	Tally	Number
vegetables	$\cancel{||||}$ $\cancel{||||}$ $\cancel{||||}$ ||	17
chicken		10
pepperoni	$\cancel{||||}$ $\cancel{||||}$ ||||	
cheese		13
mushroom	$\cancel{||||}$ ||	

1) More people prefer _____

   to _____ .

2) _____ .

3) _____ .

Reflect

As a class, complete a tally chart about your favourite subject in school.

Date:_____

Tables

1 The table shows the number of pens, pencils and rubbers on a table.

Item	Number
Pen	6
Pencil	7
Rubber	6

a) How many pens are there? ☐

b) How many pencils are there? ☐

c) There are 4 rulers. Write this in the table.

2 Holly has 10 balloons.

The table shows the patterns of the balloons.

Colour	Number
Spotty	3
Stripy	5
Plain	2

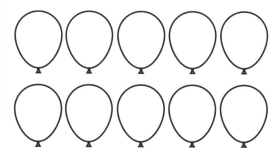

Draw the patterns on the correct number of balloons.

3 The table shows the number of animals in a pet show.

Animal	Number
Dog	8
Cat	5
Rabbit	5
Mouse	2

a) How many dogs are in the show?

b) How many rabbits and mice are in the show in total?

c) What is the total number of dogs and cats in the show?

d) What is the total number of animals in the show?

e) How many more dogs than mice are there in the show?

4 Ambika is reading a 60 page book.

The table shows how many pages she reads each day.

CHALLENGE

Day	Number of pages
Monday	12
Tuesday	20
Wednesday	15
Thursday	

By the end of Thursday she had finished the book. How many pages did Ambika read on Thursday?

Reflect

Pick a table from your lesson today.
Share with a partner some information from the table.

Date:_____

Block diagrams

1 The block diagram shows how many times children played on equipment at the park.

a) Which was the most popular equipment?

_____

_____

b) Which was the least popular equipment?

_____

c) How many times were the swings used? ☐

d) How many more times was the slide used than the horse ? ☐

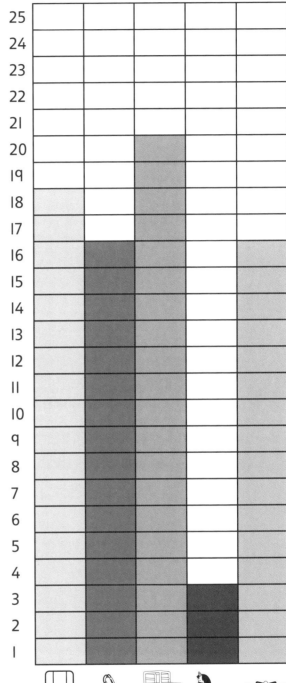

 swings
 slide
 climbing frame
 horse
roundabout

→ Textbook 2C p164

2 Children in Year 2 were asked their favourite fruit.

Use the information to complete the block diagram.

 16   8

 7   12

🍌 14

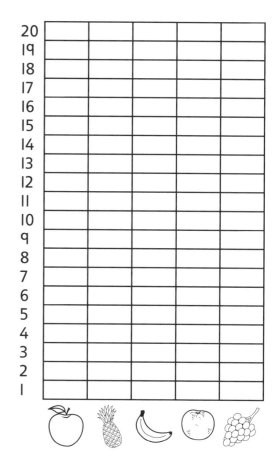

3 Children in Year 2 were asked about their dream holiday.

a) How many children said

 and altogether?

b) How many more children said

 than ?

c) Circle the third most popular holiday.

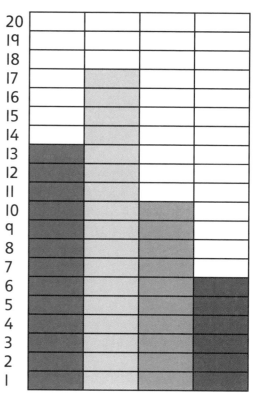

4 The diagrams show how 30 children get to school.

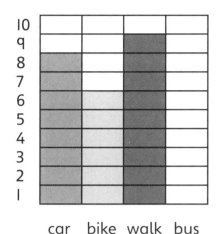

car   bike   walk   bus

Transport	Tally	Number
car		8
bike	ⅼⅼⅼⅼ ⅼ	
walk		9
bus	ⅼⅼⅼⅼ ⅼⅼ	

Complete the tally chart and the block diagram.

Reflect

Tell a partner what mistakes you can see in this block diagram.

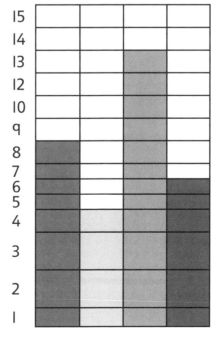

Date:_____

Draw pictograms (1 to 1)

1 **a)**

Tally these shapes.

Shape	Tally	Number
⬤		
▪		
△		

b) Draw a pictogram for the shapes.

Shape	Number
circle	
square	
triangle	

Each ✖ represents 1 shape.

2 Draw a pictogram for this table.

Leaf	Number
ash	5
beech	2
birch	3
oak	8

Leaf	Number
ash	
beech	
birch	
oak	

Each ◯ represents I leaf.

3 Circle the pictogram that shows the data in the tally chart.

Name	Tally
Sandy	̷̷̷̷̷H̷II
Ravi	II
Liv	̷̷̷̷̷H̷ I

Name	Number of goals
Sandy	⚽ ⚽
Ravi	⚽ ⚽ ⚽ ⚽ ⚽ ⚽
Liv	⚽ ⚽ ⚽ ⚽ ⚽ ⚽

Name	Number of goals
Sandy	⚽ ⚽ ⚽ ⚽ ⚽ ⚽ ⚽
Ravi	⚽ ⚽
Liv	⚽ ⚽ ⚽ ⚽ ⚽ ⚽

Each ⚽ represents I goal.

4 There are 15 children in Class A.

Here is part of a pictogram showing their favourite sports.

The rest of the children like tennis.

Complete the pictogram.

Sport	Number of children
rugby	♀♀♀♀
football	♀♀♀♀♀♀
tennis	

Each ♀ represents 1 child.

Reflect

Discuss with a partner:

What is the same about a tally chart and a pictogram?

What is different about them?

Interpret pictograms (1 to 1)

1 The pictogram shows the number of different medals won by Acorn class.

Medal colour	Number won
gold	🏅🏅🏅🏅🏅🏅🏅🏅
silver	🏅🏅🏅
bronze	🏅🏅🏅🏅🏅🏅

Each 🏅 represents 1 medal.

a) How many silver medals were won?

b) How many gold medals were won?

c) How many silver and bronze medals were won altogether?

d) How many more gold medals were won than silver medals?

e) Tell a partner how you know that more gold medals were won than bronze medals.

2 Look at the pictogram.

Flower	Number
daisy	✽ ✽ ✽ ✽ ✽ ✽ ✽
sunflower	✽ ✽ ✽ ✽ ✽ ✽ ✽ ✽ ✽
poppy	✽ ✽ ✽ ✽ ✽ ✽
tulip	✽ ✽ ✽ ✽

Each ✽ represents I flower.

a) How many sunflowers are there? ☐

b) Complete the sentences.

There are ☐ more daisies than tulips.

There are ☐ fewer poppies than sunflowers.

There are 2 fewer _____ than sunflowers.

c) How many flowers are there altogether? ☐

CHALLENGE

3 Some children were asked their favourite flavour of ice cream.

Ice cream	Number
vanilla	🍦🍦🍦🍦🍦
strawberry	🍦🍦🍦
chocolate	🍦🍦🍦🍦🍦🍦🍦

Each 🍦 represents 1 ice cream.

a) Which is the children's favourite flavour?

_____ Tell a partner how you know.

b) There are 20 children in total.

How many have not been asked yet? ▢

Reflect

Choose a pictogram from one of the Practice questions.

Tell a partner two facts about the information in the pictogram.

127

Date:_____

Draw pictograms (1 to 2, 5 or 10)

↑ Textbook 2C p176

1 **a)** Jack has four types of sticker.

Complete the numbers in the tally chart.

Sticker	Tally	Number
sun ☼	⋕⋕ |||	
smiley face ☺	||||	
rainbow ⌒	⋕⋕ ⋕⋕	
star ☆	⋕⋕		

b) Complete the pictogram to show Jack's stickers.

Sticker	Number of stickers
sun ☼	
smiley face ☺	
rainbow ⌒	
star ☆	

Each ◯ represents 2 stickers.

2 The table shows information about the weather over 50 days.

Weather	Tally	Number of days
sunny	卌 卌 卌	15
cloudy	卌 卌	
rain	卌 卌 卌 卌 卌	

a) Complete the tally chart.

b) Complete a pictogram for the tally chart.

Weather	Number of days
sunny	
cloudy	
rain	

Each ☀ represents 5 days.

c) Tell a partner why you would not draw one sun for each day.

3 Use the clues to complete the pictogram.

CHALLENGE

Child	Number of goals scored
Kira	⚽ ⚽
Hassan	
Alfie	
Lola	

Each ⚽ represents 10 goals.

Alfie scored double the number of goals scored by Kira.

Lola scored 10 more goals than Alfie.

Hassan scored 70 goals.

Reflect

When would you use 1 symbol to represent more than 1 object in a pictogram?

Discuss with a partner.

Interpret pictograms (1 to 2, 5 or 10)

1 Zeb is on a journey.

He counts different vehicles.

Vehicle	Number of vehicles
car	⊚ ⊚ ⊚ ⊚ ⊚ ⊚
lorry	⊚ ⊚
van	⊚ ⊚ ⊚ ⊚
motorbike	⊚ ⊚ ⊚

Each ⊚ represents 2 vehicles.

a) How many cars does Zeb see? ☐

b) How many motorbikes does he see? ☐

c) How many more vans does he see than lorries? ☐

d) How many vehicles does he see altogether? ☐

e) Zeb says, 'I saw four more cars than lorries.'

Is Zeb correct? _____

2 Some children voted for their favourite sweet. This pictogram shows their votes.

chew	🍬 🍬
lollipop	🍬 🍬 🍬
chocolate	🍬 🍬 🍬 🍬
marshmallow	🍬 🍬 🍬 🍬

Each 🍬 represents 10 votes.

a) Which sweet was least popular? _____

b) How many children had chew as their favourite sweet? ☐

c) How many children had marshmallow as their favourite? ☐

d) How many children were there in total? ☐

CHALLENGE

3 The pictogram shows the number of children at a summer camp.

Year 1	👦👦👦👦👦👦👦👦
Year 2	👦👦👦👦👦👦👦

Each 👦 represents 5 children.

a) How many children are in Year 1?

b) How many children are there in Year 1 and Year 2?

Tell a partner how you worked this out.

Reflect

Eddie says, 'The table in question 3 shows that there is only one more child in Year 1 than in Year 2.' Show that Eddie is incorrect.

Date:_____

End of unit check

My journal

blue	🚗 🚗 🚗 🚗 🚗
red	🚗 🚗 🚗 🚗
yellow	🚗 🚗
purple	🚗 🚗 🚗 🚗

Each 🚗 represents 5 cars.

Today I saw more purple cars than red cars.

Is Ola correct? Explain your answer.

_____

_____

Create your own sentences about this pictogram.

_____

_____

These words might help you.

equal   more than   less than

most   least   same as

difference   total

Textbook 2C p184

Power check

How do you feel about your work in this unit?

Power puzzle

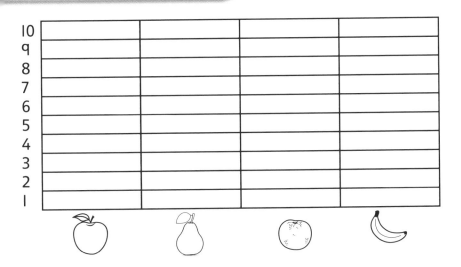

A box contains some fruit.

Try to work out how many of each fruit are in the box.

• There are 25 pieces of fruit in total.
• There are twice as many apples as pears.
• There are 2 more oranges than pears.
• There are 3 bananas.
• There are 10 apples.

Complete the block diagram to show this.

135

Published by Pearson Education Limited, 80 Strand, London, WC2R 0RL.

www.pearsonschools.co.uk

Text © Pearson Education Limited 2017, 2023
Edited by Pearson and Florence Production Ltd
First edition edited by Pearson, Little Grey Cells Publishing Services and Haremi Ltd
Designed and typeset by Pearson and PDQ Digital Media Solutions Ltd
First edition designed and typeset by Kamae Design
Original illustrations © Pearson Education Limited 2017, 2023
Illustrated by Laura Arias, Fran and David Brylewski, Nigel Dobbyn and Nadene Naude at Beehive Illustration;
Emily Skinner at Graham-Cameron Illustration; Paul Higgins at Hunter-Higgins Illustrations; and Kamae Design
Images: The Royal Mint, 1971, 1992: 9, 91, 93
Cover design by Pearson Education Ltd
Front and back cover illustrations by Will Overton at Advocate Art and Nadene Naude at Beehive Illustration

Series editor: Tony Staneff
Lead author: Josh Lury
Consultants (first edition): Professor Liu Jian and Professor Zhang Dan

The rights of Tony Staneff and Josh Lury to be identified as authors of this work have been asserted by them in accordance with the Copyright, Designs and Patents Act 1988.

First published 2017
This edition first published 2023

27 26 25 24
10 9 8 7 6

British Library Cataloguing in Publication Data
A catalogue record for this book is available from the British Library

ISBN 978 1 292 41941 1

Printed in the UK by Bell & Bain Ltd, Glasgow

For Power Maths resources go to
www.activelearnprimary.co.uk

Note from the publisher
Pearson has robust editorial processes, including answer and fact checks, to ensure the accuracy of the content in this publication, and every effort is made to ensure this publication is free of errors. We are, however, only human, and occasionally errors do occur. Pearson is not liable for any misunderstandings that arise as a result of errors in this publication, but it is our priority to ensure that the content is accurate. If you spot an error, please do contact us at resourcescorrections@pearson.com so we can make sure it is corrected.